THIS BOOK BELONGS TO

....

....

....

COVER IMAGES
(Clockwise from top left)
The Club's the Thing HENRY SANDHAM (1842-1912) Bridgeman Art Library
Golf at Pau Dorling Kindersley
Beer and Bunkers 1910 Dorling Kindersley
The Heel of Achilles Dorling Kindersley

Published in England by
FOUR SEASONS PUBLISHING LIMITED
16 ORCHARD RISE, KINGSTON UPON THAMES, SURREY KT2 7EY

Designed by Judith Pedersen
Printed in Singapore

© 2002 Four Seasons Publishing Limited

ISBN: 1 85645 162 3

GOLF SCORE
SCORE
RECORD BOOK

FOUR SEASONS
PUBLISHING

HANDICAP RECORD

Use these pages to record changes to your handicap

SSS = Standard Scratch Score **CSS** = Competition Scratch Score
NETT DIFF = Nett Differential Score, plus or minus from CSS

DATE	COURSE	COMPETITION	SSS	CSS	GROSS SCORE	NETT DIFF	EXACT H'CAP	PLAYING H'CAP

Date	Gross Score	Handicap				+5		
1 18 MAY	89	11	78	73	+3			
	88	12	76	73	-1			
			72	73				

C.F. Beater
(Signature of Handicap Secretary)

DATE	COURSE	COMPETITION	SSS	CSS	GROSS SCORE	NETT DIFF	EXACT H'CAP	PLAYING H'CAP

COMPETITIONS

Competition:

Date: .... Course: ....

Playing partner(s): ....

Score: .... Handicap: ....

Prize: ....

Remarks: ....

Competition:

Date: .... Course: ....

Playing partner(s): ....

Score: .... Handicap: ....

Prize: ....

Remarks: ....

Date	Gross Score	Handicap	Nett Score	Course		DIFFERENTIAL
1 18 MAY	89	11	78	73	+5	
	88	12	76	73	+3	
			72	73	-1	

(Signature of Handicap Secretary)

COMPETITIONS

Competition: ....

Date: .... Course: ....

Playing partner(s): ....

Score: .... Handicap: ....

Prize: ....

Remarks: ....

Competition: ....

Date: .... Course: ....

Playing partner(s): ....

Score: .... Handicap: ....

Prize: ....

Remarks: ....

COMPETITIONS

Competition: ....

Date: .... Course: ....

Playing partner(s): ....

Score: .... Handicap: ....

Prize: ....

Remarks: ....

Competition: ....

Date: .... Course: ....

Playing partner(s): ....

Score: .... Handicap: ....

Prize: ....

Remarks: ....

Date	Gross Score	Handicap	Nett Score	Course	DIFFERENTIAL
			78	73	+5
1 18 MAY	89	11	76	73	+3
	88	12	72	73	-1

C E Brace
(Signature of Handicap Secretary)

COMPETITIONS

Competition:
....

Date: .... Course: ....

Playing partner(s): ....

Score: .... Handicap: ....

Prize: ....

Remarks: ....

Competition:
....

Date: .... Course: ....

Playing partner(s): ....

Score: .... Handicap: ....

Prize: ....

Remarks: ....

HOLES IN ONE

Date: Course:

Competition:

Match type:

Weather conditions:

Playing partner(s):

Hole: Yardage:

Club used:

Shot analysis:

Celebrations:

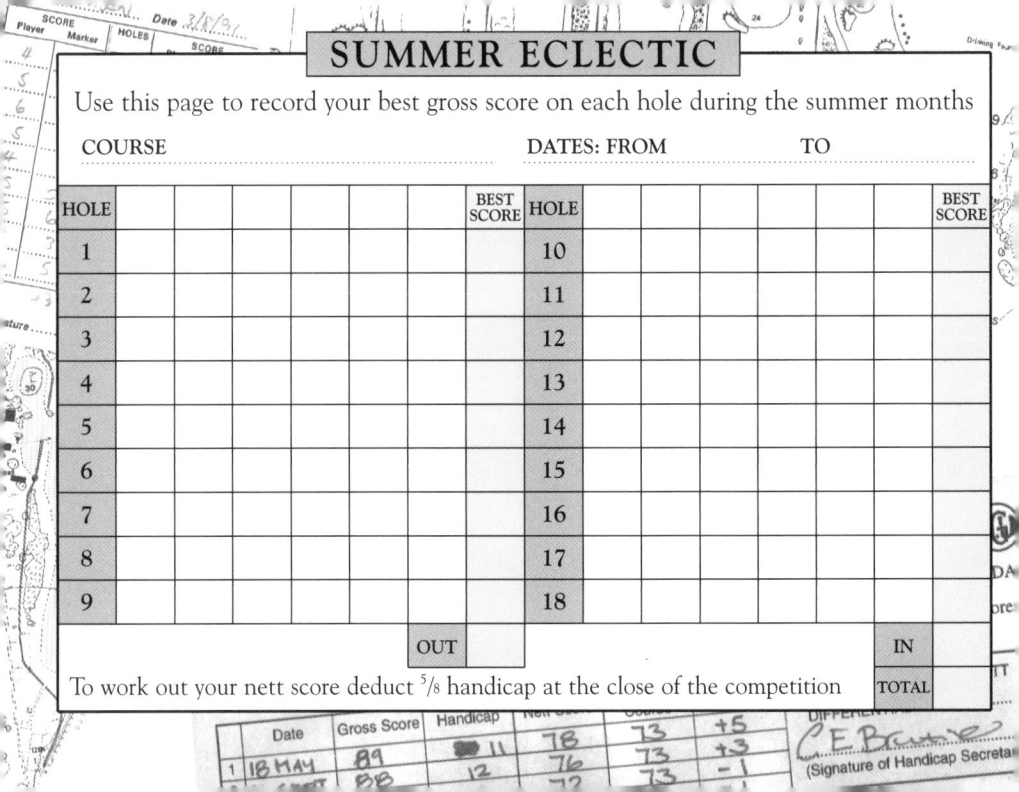

SUMMER ECLECTIC

Use this page to record your best gross score on each hole during the summer months

COURSE _____   DATES: FROM _____   TO _____

HOLE						BEST SCORE	HOLE						BEST SCORE
1							10							
2							11							
3							12							
4							13							
5							14							
6							15							
7							16							
8							17							
9							18							
					OUT								IN	
													TOTAL	

To work out your nett score deduct $\frac{5}{8}$ handicap at the close of the competition

HOLES IN ONE

Date: Course:

Competition:

Match type:

Weather conditions:

Playing partner(s):

Hole: Yardage:

Club used:

Shot analysis:

Celebrations:

WINTER ECLECTIC

Use this page to record your best gross score on each hole during the winter months

COURSE ....   DATES: FROM .... TO ....

HOLE							BEST SCORE	HOLE							BEST SCORE
1								10							
2								11							
3								12							
4								13							
5								14							
6								15							
7								16							
8								17							
9								18							
						OUT									IN	

To work out your nett score deduct 5/8 handicap at the close of the competition   **TOTAL**

TYPES OF GAMES

There are many different formats for a round of golf, depending upon the number of players, whether it is serious or just a bit of fun and also how much time is available.

STROKE PLAY (MEDAL PLAY): In stroke play, each player counts his or her total number of shots for the round. This is their gross score. To arrive at their nett score, their handicap is deducted from their gross score. Every stroke must be counted and every hole completed.

MATCH PLAY: A contest in which the players or teams attempt to win more holes than their opponents. The reckoning of holes is kept using the terms: so many 'holes up', 'all square' and so many holes 'to play'. The match is eventually won by the side that is leading by more holes than the number of holes left 'to play'. The highest possible winning margin is '10 & 8', where a team is 10 'holes up' and there are only 8 left 'to play'. A match is 'dormie' when the side is up by as many holes as there are left 'to play'. If the match is 'all square' after 18 holes, the match is 'halved'.

STABLEFORD: A type of stroke play competition (named after Dr Frank Stableford) in which points are scored in relation to the players' nett scores at each hole:

Par +2	Double bogey	0pts
Par +1	Bogey	1pt
Par		2pts

Par −1	Birdie	3pts
Par −2	Eagle	4pts
Par −3	Albatross	5pts
Par −4	Vulture	6pts

Players receive their full handicap and shots are awarded in relation to the stroke index for each hole. The gross score is recorded at each hole and the winner is the player who scores the highest number of points in total.

FOURSOME: A game in which two play against another two, in partnership, each pair playing with one ball. The pair must drive alternately. The player who drives from the first tee will play the odd holes and their partner will drive the even holes. After the drives, the players play the ball alternately. Can be played using Match Play, Stroke Play or Stableford scoring.

GREENSOME: A variation on the game of Foursome but each has their own ball. The difference is that both players in a pair drive, then choose the ball in the best position, the other ball being picked up. After that shots are played alternately. A Greensome Stableford is a popular mixed game.

SINGLE: A match for two players playing against each other. The handicap allowance is worked out as ³/₄ of the difference between the players' handicaps.

FOUR-BALL BETTER-BALL: A game for four players, which can be played as Stroke

Play, Stableford or Match Play. In Stroke Play, two competitors play as partners, each player playing their own ball. Each pair then records the better of their scores for each hole. The best nett score will be the pairing's score. If one player fails to complete the hole there is no penalty and a player who clearly cannot better their partner's nett score picks up their ball. In Match Play, two players play their better ball against the better ball of the two other players. Each player receives $^3/_4$ of the difference between their own handicap and the lowest handicap of the four.

BEST-BALL: A Stroke or Match Play game, in which the score of each individual player is matched against the better ball of the other two or the best ball of the other three players. This competition is normally only played if one player is much better than the other players.

THREESOME: A match in which one plays against two, and each side plays one ball, the twosome playing alternate shots with the same ball.

THREE-BALL: A Match Play competition in which three play against one another, each playing their own ball. Each player is playing two distinct matches.

AMERICAN STABLEFORD: A three-ball Match Play competition in which 6pts are available at each hole. If player A wins the hole and the other two players fail to complete it, A receives 6pts. If all three players halve the hole, each receives 2pts. If players A and B halve the hole, beating C, then A and B receive 3pts each and C

Date	Gross Score	Handicap	Nett	Course	Differential	
1 18 MAY	89	11	78	73	+5	C.E Br..
2 SEPT	88	12	76	73	-1	(Signature of Handicap Secretary)

receives 0pts. If player A wins the hole and players B and C halve it, A receives 4pts and B and C 1pt each. If A beats B who also beats C, A receives 4pts, B receives 2pts and C receives 0pts.

ECLECTIC: A competition run over a period of time, requiring a number of Stroke Play cards to be returned. A final total is arrived at by taking the best score on each hole from a number of Stroke Play cards returned by the same player.

TEXAS SCRAMBLE: A Stroke Play or Stableford competition, in which teams of four players tee off and then choose the ball in the best position. This ball is then marked, the other three balls are picked up and play resumes with each player playing from that position. Play continues in this way. On the green each member of the team has their chance to hole the putt. This should be a very low scoring game, with plenty of birdies and even eagles, but it may be very slow.

CROSS-COUNTRY: A game where the course is reorganised on a specific day and the holes are played in a different order and combination. This competition can be combined with a Texas Scramble.

LIMITED CLUBS: These are novelty Stroke Play or Match Play competitions in which a limit is placed on the number of clubs that can be used (e.g. only five clubs may be carried, one of which must be a putter). These competitions are especially popular in winter.

HANDICAP STROKE ALLOWANCES

Each type of competition in golf has its own alloted handicap stroke allowance. When you have chosen your game, use the table opposite to calculate the shots you will receive or give for that particular competition.

MATCH PLAY:

Singles	$3/4$ difference in handicaps
Foursomes	$3/8$ difference in combined handicaps
Greensomes	$3/4$ difference in *Greensome Medal handicaps

STROKE PLAY:

Singles	Full handicap
Foursomes	$1/2$ combined handicap

STABLEFORD COMPETITIONS:

Singles	Full handicap
Foursomes	$7/16$ combined handicaps
Greensomes	$7/8$ *Greensome Medal handicaps

ECLECTIC:

Singles	$5/8$ handicap at close of competition

* Greensome Medal Handicap – Lower handicap x 0.6 + higher handicap x 0.4.
If the handicaps are equal allow half the combined handicaps.

	Date	Gross Score	Handicap	Net		
			11	78	73	+5
1	18 MAY	89		76	73	+3
		88	12		73	-1

(Signature of Handicap Secret...)

H'CAP DIFF	3/4	7/8	3/8	7/16	H'CAP DIFF	3/4	7/8	3/8	7/16	H'CAP DIFF	3/4	7/8	3/8	7/16
1	1	1	0	0	15	11	13	6	7	29	22	25	11	13
2	2	2	1	1	16	12	14	6	7	30	23	26	11	13
3	2	3	1	1	17	13	15	6	7	31	23	27	12	14
4	3	4	2	2	18	14	16	7	8	32	24	28	12	14
5	4	4	2	2	19	14	17	7	8	33	25	29	12	14
6	5	5	2	3	20	15	18	8	9	34	26	30	13	15
7	5	6	3	3	21	16	18	8	9	35	26	31	13	15
8	6	7	3	4	22	17	19	8	10	36	27	32	14	16
9	7	8	3	4	23	17	20	9	10	37	28	32	14	16
10	8	9	4	4	24	18	21	9	11	38	29	33	14	17
11	8	10	4	5	25	19	22	9	11	39	29	34	15	17
12	9	11	5	5	26	20	23	10	11	40	30	35	15	18
13	10	11	5	6	27	20	24	10	12	41	31	36	15	18
14	11	12	5	6	28	21	25	11	12	42	32	37	16	18

Player Marker	SCORE	HOLES	SCORE

ROUND REPORT

Date: _____ Time started: _____

Course: _____

Competition: _____

Match type: _____

PLAYING PARTNERS	H'CAP
A	
B	
C	
D	

Weather conditions: _____

Best shot: _____

Hardest hole: _____

Date	Gross Score	Handicap	Nett Score	Course	DIFFERENTIAL
1 18 MAY	89	11	78	73	+5
	88	12	76	73	+3
				73	-1

C.E. Brown
(Signature of Handicap Secretary)

HOLE	YARDS	PAR	INDEX	A	B	C	D	HOLE	YARDS	PAR	INDEX	A	B	C	D
1								10							
2								11							
3								12							
4								13							
5								14							
6								15							
7								16							
8								17							
9								18							
OUT								IN							
								OUT							
								TOTAL							
								H'CAP							
								NETT							

Result:
....
....
....

ROUND REPORT

Date: .... Time started: ....

Course: ....

Competition: ....

Match type: ....

PLAYING PARTNERS	H'CAP
A	....
B	....
C	....
D	....

Weather conditions: ....

Best shot: ....

Hardest hole: ....

HOLE	YARDS	PAR	INDEX	A	B	C	D	HOLE	YARDS	PAR	INDEX	A	B	C	D
1								10							
2								11							
3								12							
4								13							
5								14							
6								15							
7								16							
8								17							
9								18							
OUT								IN							
								OUT							
								TOTAL							
								H'CAP							
								NETT							

Result:

....

....

....

ROUND REPORT

Date: Time started:

Course:

Competition:

Match type:

	PLAYING PARTNERS	H'CAP
A		
B		
C		
D		

Weather conditions:

Best shot:

Hardest hole:

HOLE	YARDS	PAR	INDEX	A	B	C	D	HOLE	YARDS	PAR	INDEX	A	B	C	D
1								10							
2								11							
3								12							
4								13							
5								14							
6								15							
7								16							
8								17							
9								18							
OUT								IN							
								OUT							
								TOTAL							
								H'CAP							
								NETT							

Result:
....
....
....

ROUND REPORT

Date: .... Time started: ....

Course: ....

Competition: ....

Match type: ....

PLAYING PARTNERS	H'CAP
A	
B	
C	
D	

Weather conditions: ....

Best shot: ....

Hardest hole: ....

Date	Gross Score	Handicap	Nett Score	Course	DIFFERENTIAL
18 MAY	89	11	78	73	+5
		12	76	73	+3
				73	-1

(Signature of Handicap Secretary)

HOLE	YARDS	PAR	INDEX	A	B	C	D	HOLE	YARDS	PAR	INDEX	A	B	C	D
1								10							
2								11							
3								12							
4								13							
5								14							
6								15							
7								16							
8								17							
9								18							
OUT								IN							

Result:

....

....

....

OUT							
TOTAL							
H'CAP							
NETT							

ROUND REPORT

Date: _____ Time started: _____

Course: _____

Competition: _____

Match type: _____

PLAYING PARTNERS	H'CAP
A	
B	
C	
D	

Weather conditions: _____

Best shot: _____

Hardest hole: _____

Date	Gross Score	Handicap	Nett Score	Course		DIFFERENTIAL
18 MAY	89	11	78	73	+5	
	88	12	76	73	+3	
				73	-1	

C.F. Beasley
(Signature of Handicap Secretary)

HOLE	YARDS	PAR	INDEX	A	B	C	D	HOLE	YARDS	PAR	INDEX	A	B	C	D
1								10							
2								11							
3								12							
4								13							
5								14							
6								15							
7								16							
8								17							
9								18							
OUT								IN							
								OUT							
								TOTAL							
								H'CAP							
								NETT							

Result:
....
....
....

ROUND REPORT

Date: Time started:

Course:

Competition:

Match type:

PLAYING PARTNERS	H'CAP
A	
B	
C	
D	

Weather conditions:

Best shot:

Hardest hole:

Date	Gross Score	Handicap	Nett Score		
			78	73	+5
18 MAY	89	11	76	73	+3
	88	12	72	73	−1

DIFFERENTIAL

C.E.B____

(Signature of Handicap Secretary)

HOLE	YARDS	PAR	INDEX	A	B	C	D	HOLE	YARDS	PAR	INDEX	A	B	C	D
1								10							
2								11							
3								12							
4								13							
5								14							
6								15							
7								16							
8								17							
9								18							
OUT								IN							

Result:
....
....
....

OUT					
TOTAL					
H'CAP					
NETT					

ROUND REPORT

Date: .... Time started: ....

Course: ....

Competition: ....

Match type: ....

PLAYING PARTNERS	H'CAP
A	....
B	....
C	....
D	....

Weather conditions: ....

Best shot: ....

Hardest hole: ....

Date	Gross Score	Handicap	Nett Score	Course		DIFFEREN...
18 MAY	89	11	78	73	+5	C F B...
	88	12	76	73	+3	
			72	73	−1	(Signature of Handicap Secreta...

HOLE	YARDS	PAR	INDEX	A	B	C	D	HOLE	YARDS	PAR	INDEX	A	B	C	D
1								10							
2								11							
3								12							
4								13							
5								14							
6								15							
7								16							
8								17							
9								18							
OUT								IN							
								OUT							
								TOTAL							
								H'CAP							
								NETT							

Result:
....
....
....

ROUND REPORT

Date: .... Time started: ....

Course: ....

Competition: ....

Match type: ....

PLAYING PARTNERS	H'CAP
A	
B	
C	
D	

Weather conditions: ....

Best shot: ....

Hardest hole: ....

HOLE	YARDS	PAR	INDEX	A	B	C	D	HOLE	YARDS	PAR	INDEX	A	B	C	D
1								10							
2								11							
3								12							
4								13							
5								14							
6								15							
7								16							
8								17							
9								18							
OUT								IN							
								OUT							
								TOTAL							
								H'CAP							
								NETT							

Result:
....
....
....

ROUND REPORT

Date: .... Time started: ....

Course: ....

Competition: ....

Match type: ....

PLAYING PARTNERS	H'CAP
A	
B	
C	
D	

Weather conditions: ....

Best shot: ....

Hardest hole: ....

HOLE	YARDS	PAR	INDEX	A	B	C	D	HOLE	YARDS	PAR	INDEX	A	B	C	D
1								10							
2								11							
3								12							
4								13							
5								14							
6								15							
7								16							
8								17							
9								18							
OUT								IN							
								OUT							
								TOTAL							
								H'CAP							
								NETT							

Result:
....
....
....

ROUND REPORT

Date: .... Time started: ....

Course: ....

Competition: ....

Match type: ....

PLAYING PARTNERS	H'CAP
A	
B	
C	
D	

Weather conditions: ....

Best shot: ....

Hardest hole: ....

Date	Gross Score	Handicap	Nett Score		
18 MAY	89	11	78	73	+5
	88	12	76	73	+3
			72	73	-1

HOLE	YARDS	PAR	INDEX	A	B	C	D	HOLE	YARDS	PAR	INDEX	A	B	C	D
1								10							
2								11							
3								12							
4								13							
5								14							
6								15							
7								16							
8								17							
9								18							
OUT								IN							
								OUT							
								TOTAL							
								H'CAP							
								NETT							

Result:

....

....

....

ROUND REPORT

Date: .... Time started: ....

Course: ....

Competition: ....

Match type: ....

PLAYING PARTNERS	H'CAP
A	
B	
C	
D	

Weather conditions: ....

Best shot: ....

Hardest hole: ....

Date	Gross Score	Handicap	Nett Score	Course	DIFFERENTIAL
18 MAY	89	11	78	73	+5
	88	12	76	73	+3
			72	73	-1

(Signature of Handicap Secreta...)

HOLE	YARDS	PAR	INDEX	A	B	C	D	HOLE	YARDS	PAR	INDEX	A	B	C	D
1								10							
2								11							
3								12							
4								13							
5								14							
6								15							
7								16							
8								17							
9								18							
OUT								IN							
								OUT							
								TOTAL							
								H'CAP							
								NETT							

Result:

....

....

....

ROUND REPORT

Date: .... Time started: ....

Course: ....

Competition: ....

Match type: ....

PLAYING PARTNERS	H'CAP
A	....
B	....
C	....
D	....

Weather conditions: ....

Best shot: ....

Hardest hole: ....

HOLE	YARDS	PAR	INDEX	A	B	C	D	HOLE	YARDS	PAR	INDEX	A	B	C	D
1								10							
2								11							
3								12							
4								13							
5								14							
6								15							
7								16							
8								17							
9								18							
OUT								IN							

Result:

....

....

....

OUT			
TOTAL			
H'CAP			
NETT			

ROUND REPORT

Date: Time started:

Course:

Competition:

Match type:

PLAYING PARTNERS	H'CAP
A	
B	
C	
D	

Weather conditions:

Best shot:

Hardest hole:

Date	Gross Score	Handicap	Nett Score	Course	
18 MAY	89	11	78	73	+5
	89	13	76	73	+3
				73	−1

HOLE	YARDS	PAR	INDEX	A	B	C	D	HOLE	YARDS	PAR	INDEX	A	B	C	D
1								10							
2								11							
3								12							
4								13							
5								14							
6								15							
7								16							
8								17							
9								18							
OUT								IN							
								OUT							
								TOTAL							
								H'CAP							
								NETT							

Result:
....
....
....

ROUND REPORT

Date: .... Time started: ....

Course: ....

Competition: ....

Match type: ....

PLAYING PARTNERS	H'CAP
A	....
B	....
C	....
D	....

Weather conditions: ....

Best shot: ....

Hardest hole: ....

HOLE	YARDS	PAR	INDEX	A	B	C	D	HOLE	YARDS	PAR	INDEX	A	B	C	D
1								10							
2								11							
3								12							
4								13							
5								14							
6								15							
7								16							
8								17							
9								18							
OUT								IN							
								OUT							
								TOTAL							
								H'CAP							
								NETT							

Result:

....

....

ROUND REPORT

Date: .... Time started: ....

Course: ....

Competition: ....

Match type: ....

PLAYING PARTNERS	H'CAP
A	
B	
C	
D	

Weather conditions: ....

Best shot: ....

Hardest hole: ....

HOLE	YARDS	PAR	INDEX	A	B	C	D	HOLE	YARDS	PAR	INDEX	A	B	C	D
1								10							
2								11							
3								12							
4								13							
5								14							
6								15							
7								16							
8								17							
9								18							
OUT								IN							
								OUT							
								TOTAL							
								H'CAP							
								NETT							

Result:
....
....
....

ROUND REPORT

Date: .... Time started: ....

Course: ....

Competition: ....

Match type: ....

PLAYING PARTNERS	H'CAP
A	....
B	....
C	....
D	....

Weather conditions: ....

Best shot: ....

Hardest hole: ....

HOLE	YARDS	PAR	INDEX	A	B	C	D	HOLE	YARDS	PAR	INDEX	A	B	C	D
1								10							
2								11							
3								12							
4								13							
5								14							
6								15							
7								16							
8								17							
9								18							
OUT								IN							
								OUT							
								TOTAL							
								H'CAP							
								NETT							

Result:
....
....
....

ROUND REPORT

Date: .... Time started: ....

Course: ....

Competition: ....

Match type: ....

PLAYING PARTNERS	H'CAP
A	
B	
C	
D	

Weather conditions: ....

Best shot: ....

Hardest hole: ....

HOLE	YARDS	PAR	INDEX	A	B	C	D		HOLE	YARDS	PAR	INDEX	A	B	C	D
1									10							
2									11							
3									12							
4									13							
5									14							
6									15							
7									16							
8									17							
9									18							
OUT									IN							

Result:

....

....

....

OUT				
TOTAL				
H'CAP				
NETT				

ROUND REPORT

Date: .... Time started: ....

Course: ....

Competition: ....

Match type: ....

PLAYING PARTNERS	H'CAP
A	
B	
C	
D	

Weather conditions: ....

Best shot: ....

Hardest hole: ....

HOLE	YARDS	PAR	INDEX	A	B	C	D	HOLE	YARDS	PAR	INDEX	A	B	C	D
1								10							
2								11							
3								12							
4								13							
5								14							
6								15							
7								16							
8								17							
9								18							
OUT								IN							

Result:

....

....

....

OUT							
TOTAL							
H'CAP							
NETT							

ROUND REPORT

Date: .... Time started: ....

Course: ....

Competition: ....

Match type: ....

PLAYING PARTNERS	H'CAP
A	....
B	....
C	....
D	....

Weather conditions: ....

Best shot: ....

Hardest hole: ....

HOLE	YARDS	PAR	INDEX	A	B	C	D	HOLE	YARDS	PAR	INDEX	A	B	C	D
1								10							
2								11							
3								12							
4								13							
5								14							
6								15							
7								16							
8								17							
9								18							
OUT								IN							
Result:								OUT							
								TOTAL							
								H'CAP							
								NETT							

ROUND REPORT

Date: Time started:

Course:

Competition:

Match type:

	PLAYING PARTNERS	H'CAP
A		
B		
C		
D		

Weather conditions:

Best shot:

Hardest hole:

Date	Gross Score	Handicap	Nett Score	Course		DIFFERENTIAL
					+5	
18 MAY	89	11	78	73	+3	
	88	12	76	73	-1	

C E Brady

(Signature of Handicap Secretary)

HOLE	YARDS	PAR	INDEX	A	B	C	D	HOLE	YARDS	PAR	INDEX	A	B	C	D
1								10							
2								11							
3								12							
4								13							
5								14							
6								15							
7								16							
8								17							
9								18							
OUT								IN							

Result:
....
....
....

OUT							
TOTAL							
H'CAP							
NETT							

ROUND REPORT

Date: .... Time started: ....

Course: ....

Competition: ....

Match type: ....

PLAYING PARTNERS	H'CAP
A	....
B	....
C	....
D	....

Weather conditions: ....

Best shot: ....

Hardest hole: ....

HOLE	YARDS	PAR	INDEX	A	B	C	D	HOLE	YARDS	PAR	INDEX	A	B	C	D
1								10							
2								11							
3								12							
4								13							
5								14							
6								15							
7								16							
8								17							
9								18							
OUT								IN							
								OUT							
								TOTAL							
								H'CAP							
								NETT							

Result:

....

....

....

117	3	106	5	5	5	—	305	4
337	4	321	17	4	3	0	349	4
462	4	321	11	4	4	0	113	3
521		439	1	5			322	

1④ 337 yds   2④ 370 yds 3.④ 418 yds

ROUND REPORT

Date: .... Time started: ....

Course: ....

Competition: ....

Match type: ....

PLAYING PARTNERS	H'CAP
A	....
B	....
C	....
D	....

Weather conditions: ....

Best shot: ....

Hardest hole: ....

Date	Gross Score	Handicap	Nett Score	Course		
				73	+5	
18 MAY	89	11	78	73	+3	
	88	12	76	73	-1	

(Signature of Handicap Secreta

HOLE	YARDS	PAR	INDEX	A	B	C	D	HOLE	YARDS	PAR	INDEX	A	B	C	D
1								10							
2								11							
3								12							
4								13							
5								14							
6								15							
7								16							
8								17							
9								18							
OUT								IN							
Result:								OUT							
								TOTAL							
								H'CAP							
								NETT							

ROUND REPORT

Date: .... Time started: ....

Course: ....

Competition: ....

Match type: ....

PLAYING PARTNERS	H'CAP
A	
B	
C	
D	

Weather conditions: ....

Best shot: ....

Hardest hole: ....

HOLE	YARDS	PAR	INDEX	A	B	C	D	HOLE	YARDS	PAR	INDEX	A	B	C	D
1								10							
2								11							
3								12							
4								13							
5								14							
6								15							
7								16							
8								17							
9								18							
OUT								IN							
								OUT							
								TOTAL							
								H'CAP							
								NETT							

Result:

ROUND REPORT

Date: .... Time started: ....

Course: ....

Competition: ....

Match type: ....

PLAYING PARTNERS	H'CAP
A	....
B	....
C	....
D	....

Weather conditions: ....

Best shot: ....

Hardest hole: ....

HOLE	YARDS	PAR	INDEX	A	B	C	D	HOLE	YARDS	PAR	INDEX	A	B	C	D
1								10							
2								11							
3								12							
4								13							
5								14							
6								15							
7								16							
8								17							
9								18							
OUT								IN							
Result:								OUT							
								TOTAL							
								H'CAP							
								NETT							

ROUND REPORT

Date: .... Time started: ....

Course: ....

Competition: ....

Match type: ....

PLAYING PARTNERS	H'CAP
A	
B	
C	
D	

Weather conditions: ....

Best shot: ....

Hardest hole: ....

Date	Gross Score	Handicap	Nett Score		DIFFEREN
				73	+5
18 MAY	89	11	78	73	+3
	88	12	76	73	-1

(Signature of Handicap Secreta

HOLE	YARDS	PAR	INDEX	A	B	C	D	HOLE	YARDS	PAR	INDEX	A	B	C	D
1								10							
2								11							
3								12							
4								13							
5								14							
6								15							
7								16							
8								17							
9								18							
OUT								IN							

Result:
....
....
....

IN							
OUT							
TOTAL							
H'CAP							
NETT							

ROUND REPORT

Date: .... Time started: ....

Course: ....

Competition: ....

Match type: ....

	PLAYING PARTNERS	H'CAP
A	....	....
B	....	....
C	....	....
D	....	....

Weather conditions: ....

Best shot: ....

Hardest hole: ....

Date	Gross Score	Handicap	Nett Score	Course	DIFFERENTIAL
18 MAY	89	11	78	73	+5
		12	76	73	+3
			73		-1

HOLE	YARDS	PAR	INDEX	A	B	C	D	HOLE	YARDS	PAR	INDEX	A	B	C	D
1								10							
2								11							
3								12							
4								13							
5								14							
6								15							
7								16							
8								17							
9								18							
OUT								IN							
Result:								OUT							
								TOTAL							
								H'CAP							
								NETT							

ROUND REPORT

Date: .... Time started: ....

Course: ....

Competition: ....

Match type: ....

PLAYING PARTNERS	H'CAP
A	....
B	....
C	....
D	....

Weather conditions: ....

Best shot: ....

Hardest hole: ....

Muswell Hill   1/2/91   5ee dned   E.D.S. Hcp. Initials of Hcp Sec.

5 3 91 73   9

HOLE	YARDS	PAR	INDEX	A	B	C	D	HOLE	YARDS	PAR	INDEX	A	B	C	D
1								10							
2								11							
3								12							
4								13							
5								14							
6								15							
7								16							
8								17							
9								18							
OUT								IN							
Result:								OUT							
								TOTAL							
								H'CAP							
								NETT							

ROUND REPORT

Date: .... Time started: ....

Course: ....

Competition: ....

Match type: ....

PLAYING PARTNERS	H'CAP
A	....
B	....
C	....
D	....

Weather conditions: ....

Best shot: ....

Hardest hole: ....

HOLE	YARDS	PAR	INDEX	A	B	C	D	HOLE	YARDS	PAR	INDEX	A	B	C	D
1								10							
2								11							
3								12							
4								13							
5								14							
6								15							
7								16							
8								17							
9								18							
OUT								IN							

Result:

....

....

....

OUT							
TOTAL							
H'CAP							
NETT							

ROUND REPORT

Date: Time started:

Course:

Competition:

Match type:

PLAYING PARTNERS	H'CAP
A	
B	
C	
D	

Weather conditions:

Best shot:

Hardest hole:

HOLE	YARDS	PAR	INDEX	A	B	C	D	HOLE	YARDS	PAR	INDEX	A	B	C	D
1								10							
2								11							
3								12							
4								13							
5								14							
6								15							
7								16							
8								17							
9								18							
OUT								IN							
								OUT							
								TOTAL							
								H'CAP							
								NETT							

Result:

....

....

....

ROUND REPORT

Date: .... Time started: ....

Course: ....

Competition: ....

Match type: ....

PLAYING PARTNERS	H'CAP
A	
B	
C	
D	

Weather conditions: ....

Best shot: ....

Hardest hole: ....

Date	Gross Score	Handicap	Nett Score	Course		
18 MAY	89	11	78	73	+5	
	88	12	76	73	+3	
			72	73	−1	

DIFFERENTIAL

C.F.Bates

(Signature of Handicap Secretary)

Muswell Hill   1/2/91   see final   E.D.S.   Hcp.   Initials of Hcp Sec.

5 3 91   73   70   9

HOLE	YARDS	PAR	INDEX	A	B	C	D	HOLE	YARDS	PAR	INDEX	A	B	C	D
1								10							
2								11							
3								12							
4								13							
5								14							
6								15							
7								16							
8								17							
9								18							
OUT								IN							
								OUT							
								TOTAL							
								H'CAP							
								NETT							

Result:
....
....
....

117	3	352	5		305	4	
337	4	106	17		349	4	
462	4	321	11		113	3	
521	5	439	1		322	4	

337yds   370yds   418yds

ROUND REPORT

Date: Time started:

Course:

Competition:

Match type:

PLAYING PARTNERS	**H'CAP**
A	
B	
C	
D	

Weather conditions:

Best shot:

Hardest hole:

Date	Gross Score	Handicap	Nett Score	Course	DIFFERENTIAL
18 MAY	89	11	78	73	+5
	88	12	76	73	+3
SEPT			72	73	−1

C.E.B... (Signature of Handicap Secretary)

Kernei 7/2/91
Muswell Hill 5 3 91
Score
Diff
Comp/
E.D.S.
Hcp.
Initials of
Hcp. Sec.
73
9
K
Joueur

HOLE	YARDS	PAR	INDEX	A	B	C	D	HOLE	YARDS	PAR	INDEX	A	B	C	D
1								10							
2								11							
3								12							
4								13							
5								14							
6								15							
7								16							
8								17							
9								18							
OUT								IN							

Result:
....
....
....

OUT	
TOTAL	
H'CAP	
NETT	

ROUND REPORT

Date: Time started:

Course:

Competition:

Match type:

	PLAYING PARTNERS	H'CAP
A		
B		
C		
D		

Weather conditions:

Best shot:

Hardest hole:

HOLE	YARDS	PAR	INDEX	A	B	C	D	HOLE	YARDS	PAR	INDEX	A	B	C	D
1								10							
2								11							
3								12							
4								13							
5								14							
6								15							
7								16							
8								17							
9								18							
OUT								IN							
Result:								OUT							
								TOTAL							
								H'CAP							
								NETT							

ROUND REPORT

Date: .... Time started: ....

Course: ....

Competition: ....

Match type: ....

PLAYING PARTNERS	H'CAP
A	....
B	....
C	....
D	....

Weather conditions: ....

Best shot: ....

Hardest hole: ....

HOLE	YARDS	PAR	INDEX	A	B	C	D	HOLE	YARDS	PAR	INDEX	A	B	C	D
1								10							
2								11							
3								12							
4								13							
5								14							
6								15							
7								16							
8								17							
9								18							
OUT								IN							
Result:								OUT							
								TOTAL							
								H'CAP							
								NETT							

ROUND REPORT

Date: Time started:

Course:

Competition:

Match type:

PLAYING PARTNERS	H'CAP
A	
B	
C	
D	

Weather conditions:

Best shot:

Hardest hole:

Date	Gross Score	Handicap	Nett Score	Course		DIFFERENTIAL
18 MAY	89	11	78	73	+5	
	88	12	76	73	+3	
			72	73	-1	

HOLE	YARDS	PAR	INDEX	A	B	C	D	HOLE	YARDS	PAR	INDEX	A	B	C	D
1								10							
2								11							
3								12							
4								13							
5								14							
6								15							
7								16							
8								17							
9								18							
OUT								IN							
								OUT							
								TOTAL							
								H'CAP							
								NETT							

Result:
....
....
....

ROUND REPORT

Date: .... Time started: ....

Course: ....

Competition: ....

Match type: ....

PLAYING PARTNERS	H'CAP
A	....
B	....
C	....
D	....

Weather conditions: ....

Best shot: ....

Hardest hole: ....

Date	Gross Score	Handicap	Nett Score	Course	DIFFERENTIAL
18 MAY	89	11	78	73	+5
			76	73	+3
SEPT	88	12	72	73	−1

C.E. Brunner (Signature of Handicap Secretary)

HOLE	YARDS	PAR	INDEX	A	B	C	D	HOLE	YARDS	PAR	INDEX	A	B	C	D
1								10							
2								11							
3								12							
4								13							
5								14							
6								15							
7								16							
8								17							
9								18							
OUT								IN							
Result:								OUT							
								TOTAL							
								H'CAP							
								NETT							

ROUND REPORT

Date: .... Time started: ....

Course: ....

Competition: ....

Match type: ....

PLAYING PARTNERS	H'CAP
A	....
B	....
C	....
D	....

Weather conditions: ....

Best shot: ....

Hardest hole: ....

HOLE	YARDS	PAR	INDEX	A	B	C	D	HOLE	YARDS	PAR	INDEX	A	B	C	D
1								10							
2								11							
3								12							
4								13							
5								14							
6								15							
7								16							
8								17							
9								18							
OUT								IN							
Result:								OUT							
								TOTAL							
								H'CAP							
								NETT